Shakespeare Tales

Macbeth

First published 2016 by

Bloomsbury Education, an imprint of Bloomsbury Publishing Plc
50 Bedford Square, London, WC1B 3DP

www.bloomsbury.com

A CIP catalogue for this book is available from the British Library

ISBN: 978-1-4729-1780-5 (paperback)

Printed and Bound by CPI Group (UK) Ltd, Croydon CR0 4YY

1 3 5 7 9 10 8 6 4 2

TERRY DEARY

Shakespeare Tales

Macbeth

Illustrated by

Tambe

BLOOMSBURY EDUCATION
AN IMPRINT OF BLOOMSBURY
LONDON OXFORD NEW YORK NEW DELHI SYDNEY

Contents

The pot-girl's tale

So much blood. It was splashed across the stage when the actors showed the play they called 'Macbeth'. It splattered on the walls and the costumes, the swords and the shoes. It even hit one of the watching women in the eye one evening. (How she screamed. How I laughed.)

It was pig's blood of course. They kept it in a bucket by the side of the stage and dipped their daggers in it before each scene to make the fights look real. (I mean they kept the blood in a bucket … not a pig. Sorry. This writing is much harder than I thought. But I need to tell you my story.)

The audience loved all the stabbing and the fighting. But no one stopped to ask one question. 'Who clears up the blood?' I'm sure Master Shakespeare never thought about that when he wrote the play.

I could have told them, 'It's me. It's not really my job. I am Mary, a pot-girl at the White Swan Inn. I gather the empty ale pots and wine cups from the wooden tables. Then I fill them and take them to the rowdy drinkers with bad teeth and worse breath. Sometime they give me a penny or two. Mostly they ignore me like the sawdust on the floor. The sawdust I had to sweep up every night with the spilled beer and spit.

But once a year the players came to the White Swan. They set up a stage in the stable-yard and the customers took their ale out to watch the plays. They were the most exciting thing that ever happened in my life. They players let me try on their wonderful costumes and spoke to me like a young lady, not an orphan serving girl. They let me sweep the stage after their show and paid me a groat every night.

I thought they were magic and they made me feel like the richest woman in England.

But that summer of 1605 – the year the Powder Plotters tries to blow up King James – the actors brought a play about another Scottish King called Macbeth.

And that play didn't have dust to sweep and lost buttons to find. It had blood and I had to swill it off the stage with water. And that's what caused so much trouble with my master – Dick Fulbright – or Foulbrew as some of his customers called him when he sold them bad ale.

At first I served the ale and found time to watch the play. It was creepy and cruel. Let me tell you the terrible tale of King Macbeth ...

Witches and war
The play

Scotland long ago

King Duncan of Scotland is old. Too old. Too weak to carry on, some say. A group of rebel lords all want his throne. The traitors gather soldiers from across the seas. The fierce and fearsome fighters land on Scotland's shores.

Duncan is far too frail to fight so, when these enemies invade, he leaves the fighting to his warrior chief, Macbeth. Macbeth, the hero captain, battles bravely. He executes one enemy – cutting him in half – and drives the foes of Scotland into the sea.

The battle's done. The weary warrior Macbeth sets off for home. His loyal friend, Banquo, marches back beside him through the evening mists of fog and filthy air.

They reach a bleak and misty moor where three shapeless figures lurk. The shadowy witches cast spells over a bubbling brew of bad magic. The cackleand crow as they throw in sickening scraps.

Macbeth and Banquo find that the weird sisters claim to see away into the future. They call Macbeth, 'The Lord of Cawdor.'

'The Lord of Cawdor's still alive. How can I be Lord of Cawdor?' the gallant captain asks.

'Oh, you will be, very soon,' they cackle, 'And you are the future King of Scotland.' Next, they turn their wrinkled faces to Banquo. 'When Macbeth dies then your son will be the next to rule.'

And then the witches seem to melt into the air just as raindrops vanish when they hit a pond. Macbeth is shaken. 'I'm not the Lord of Cawdor,' he tells Banquo, 'So those weird creatures were just a dream. I'll not be King of Scotland.'

Just then a soldier arrives with great news. King Duncan has found that the Lord of Cawdor was one of the rebels who fought with the invaders. The King has sentenced Cawdor to die. Macbeth, the faithful fighter, is to be the next Lord of Cawdor.

Macbeth rides home and tells his wife the strange things he has seen. His lady burns as fiery as a castle torch and cries with happiness. 'The weird women

said that you'll be Lord of Cawdor ... and you are?'

'They did and I am,' Macbeth says.

'They said that you'd be King, so it will be ... and I'll be Queen,' she says.

But Macbeth shakes his head. 'Old King Duncan's still alive, he says. 'He's weak, but he's not sick. He plans to visit us tomorrow. You'll see that he's well.'

Lady Macbeth bites a nail and slyly says, 'He may be well when he arrives ... but he'll be dead before he leaves. Leave it all to me.'

The King arrives. Macbeth seems

overjoyed to see his guest. Yet he's afraid to use his knife, he tells his wife when they're alone. Macbeth can kill a man in war but shudders at the thought of slaughtering his friend, the King. His lady tells her plan

The King will go to bed. She will give the guards hot wine with drugs in it and they will fall asleep outside the King's bedroom door. Macbeth can then slip past and plunge two daggers into the King's body.

And, when the King is dead, Macbeth must place the blood-stained daggers on the guards so they will get the blame.

'We will not fail if you are brave enough, Macbeth,' the lady says.

And so the King must die that night.

The pot-girl's tale

The actors took a short break and the audience refilled their ale pots. As soon as that scene ended it seemed that two hundred people wanted me to fill their mugs from my large jug.

I trotted as quickly as I could between the bawling drinkers. If I forgot to take their money then Master Foulbrew would take payment from the pennies he gave me. If I spilled his muddy ale on the sawdust he would take payment from my pennies too. And if I was too slow to serve a hundred drinkers in that short break ... he'd do worse. He'd take the long belt from his wide waist and thrash me.

That evening I even found time to fill the ale pots of the actors. The boy playing Lady Macbeth, Henry, gave me two groats and told me to keep the change.

He was so handsome, yet when he played

that cruel lady he made me tremble and shake with fear. Master Shakespeare, the man who wrote the play, said the boy was the best he'd seen and when they played this Scottish play for King James, the new King, then the King might give Henry a purse packed with gold.

I'd never seen a purse packed with gold. While I was washing pots for Foulbrew I knew I'd never earn one.

Blood and bells

The play

Macbeth's castle at night

Night falls, as dark as a midnight well. Macbeth waits for his wife to ring the bell that will tell him Duncan's guards are deep asleep. He has a waking nightmare of a dagger hanging in the air in front of him. He is sick at the thought of killing a sleeping king.

The bell rings. He gathers the daggers and sighs, 'I go, and it is done; **the bell**

invites me. I hope it doesn't wake you, Duncan, for it is your funeral bell.'

As he leaves to do the evil deed Lady Macbeth paces the floor of her room, fierce-eyed and breathless, waiting for her husband to return. But when he comes she sees him carrying the knives, dripping blood. He should have left them with the guards. The fool!

The pot-girl's tale

The actor playing Macbeth had stepped through the curtains on the right of the stage with the daggers shining in the torchlight. The midnight darkness was all in our mind. Henry, playing Lady Macbeth, entered from the other side.

He hissed his joy that soon he would be Queen. It seemed the watching crowd stopped breathing – frightened by this ruthless woman, waiting to see if her plan had worked.

That was when Macbeth took the shining daggers and dipped them in the bucket of pig's blood. I have seen some groups of actors who put red paint on their weapons to show they'd been used to stab someone. But Master Shakespeare said he wanted real blood that dripped from the daggers and smelled of death.

And that scene would be my first with the mop. I grabbed it and waited ready to clean the stage as soon as the scene was ended. I felt the hot breath in my ear as Master Foulbrew hissed, 'Why aren't you serving ale girl? You're here to serve the customers not watch a play.'

'Sorry master Fulbright, but you told me to mop the stage after every scene so it isn't stained with blood,' I said quietly. I didn't dare argue too strongly.

The innkeeper growled low. 'Then why aren't you mopping the stage? I've a mind to take my belt to your back and thrash you till you bleed!'

'Lady Macbeth is raging at her husband,' I whispered, 'because he's brought the knives from the murder room so everyone will know they did it.'

'Foolish Macbeth,' Foulbrew muttered.

'They can't have a pot-girl wandering on with a mop and bucket.'

He nodded. 'I suppose not. Get on there and mop the stage as soon as they've finished.'

'That's a good idea,' I murmured.

He shook his head wisely. 'Fancy bringing the daggers away from the murder. I'd have left them there. What a stupid thing to do.' He snorted and walked away. 'I could write a better play than that.'

The play

Macbeth's castle

Lady Macbeth tells her husband to take the daggers back to the dead king's bedroom.

'I can't,' he groans. 'I can't go back to that dreadful place after what I've done.'

The lady sneers, 'Weakling. Give me the daggers.' She snatches them from Macbeth and goes off to wipe the blades on the sleeves of the guards and leave the weapons by their sides.

Next morning Lord Macduff calls to see the King and finds him dead. 'Murder! Treason!' he cries. 'Sound the bell to tell the world. The King is dead. Murdered in his bed.'

Macbeth rushes out and returns to tell the frightened lords a mighty lie; he says the guards were found with blood upon their hands – they must have killed the King – and so Macbeth killed both the guards. The dead guards get the blame for Macbeth's wicked deeds.

The King's son, Malcolm, thinks that he'll be blamed – he's sure the Scots will say he paid the guards to kill the King so he can take his father's throne. Frightened Malcolm rides away to England. That leaves

the crown for Scotland's greatest warrior to wear. The new King is ... Macbeth.

And so the witches' words came true.

Murderer Macbeth is King of all the Scots.

Guests and ghosts
The play

Scotland long ago

Macbeth rules but lives in fear. Fear that he will be found out. Fear of shadows, fear of foes but, mostly, fear of friends. Banquo saw the meeting with the witches.

Banquo starts to think Macbeth could be a killer, so Banquo has to die. Macbeth sends a gang of cut-throats to kill his friend as he rides to Lady Macbeth's feast

Banquo dies but his son escapes. And then the feast. And what a feast of horror it turns out to be ...

The pot-girl's tale

The stage helpers hurried to place tables and chairs on the stage and fill them with dishes and stale food that no one would ever eat.

As they set the scene I hurried from customer to customer with the ale jug to fill up their pots and gather their pennies into my apron. The pocket was heavy with money and clinked as I ran across the yard.

Some customers wanted the mutton stew – fat and foul brew like something

from the pot of Macbeth's witches. I knew Master Foulbrew made it from sheep that had died of old age. And if any stray cats or dogs wandered into the White Swan they could end up in the pot too.

I knew this would be another scene that would need my mop. Banquo was dead and the actor who played him was splashing blood onto this hands and face as he stood behind the curtain waiting to enter. This was the scene that would put the mutton-eaters off their meal. I had to smile. Master Foulbrew glared at me. 'What have you got to laugh at you worm?' he snarled.

'I'm just so happy to be working for you, Master,' I said. His red eyes glowed with hate.

The play

Macbeth's castle

Macbeth cries, 'A hearty welcome to you all.'

The lords all sit down at the table. They tell King Macbeth to take his seat and join them. 'The table's full,' he tells them

A lord points to an empty seat and says, 'No. Here's a place.'

'Is this a trick?' the king cries. For in that empty seat he thinks he's seeing Banquo's blood-soaked ghost and shouts, 'Don't glare at me that way; it wasn't me that had you killed.'

The guests are frightened. They think King Macbeth has lost his wits. Lady Macbeth tells them, 'Don't worry friends, he's been like this since he was young. He'll soon get over it.' She hisses at her husband, 'Sit down now. There's nothing there.'

'I saw him,' he moans, 'Sure as I am standing here.'

The guests all leave – the great lords of Scotland. They're now quite sure their King is mad – he isn't fit to rule their land. The lords have turned to Duncan's son, Malcolm, to lead the rebels. Macbeth must raise an army if he wants to hold on to his crown.

He must seek help. Tomorrow he will go back to the heath. He'll meet up with the witches. They will tell him what to do.

There on the lonely moors the witches huddle round their cauldron, casting spells.

Snakes and Smoke
The play

A Scotish moor

Macbeth marches to the moors where he last saw the witches. They are brewing slices of swamp snake, poison from toads, scales from a dragon and tooth from a wolf, as they chant ...

'Eye of newt and toe of frog,
Wool of bat and tongue of dog,
Adder's fork and blind-worm's sting,
Lizard's leg and owlet's wing,
For a charm of powerful trouble,
Like a hell-broth boil and bubble.
Double, double toil and trouble,
Fire burn and cauldron bubble.'

The pot-girl's tale

When they reached the last part of the spell a witch screeched, 'Cool it with a baboon's blood, Then the charm is firm and good.'

Some ale-filled fool in the audience shouted out, 'Bet that tastes just like Fulbright's mutton stew!'

The audience roared with laughter at the very moment they were supposed to be shivering with horror. The actors playing the witches looked up and watched with open mouths as Master Foulbrew pushed through the audience, grabbed the drinker by the collar and dragged him out of the door and into the street. The audience cheered. The actors tried to carry on.

The play

The witches' lair

'What are you doing, you black and midnight hags?' Macbeth asks. 'You read my future once. Do it again.'

Out of the cauldron twisted wisps of smoke form into foul faces that speak to him. One warns him: 'Beware of Lord Macduff.'

'I'll kill him,' Macbeth cries. 'I'll kill him and his family.'

Another smoky figure speaks, 'Macbeth will never be defeated till Birnam Wood marches to fight at Dunsinane Hill.'

'A wood that marches to meet me in a battle?' That makes Macbeth laugh. 'That will never be.'

But the last phantom figure in the mist is Banquo ... dripping blood. Again that ghost has come to haunt him.

The witches disappear. And Macbeth makes his plans to kill Macduff. But Lord Macduff has run away to England. There he plans to raise an army and return to fight Macbeth.

So King Macbeth takes his revenge by sending killers to Macduff's castle where they slaughter his wife and children.

The pot-girl's tale

Yes, more blood as the Macduff family died. It was hardly worth mopping the blood after Banquo's dripping ghost. The killing of Lady Macduff and the children scattered more.

There was another break and Master Foulbrew served his own ale while I mopped the stage.

I'd watched the play all week. I knew the worst was yet to come.

Broadswords and battle

The pot-girl's tale

Lady Macbeth went mad. She felt so guilty about all the people who had died so that she could become queen. Then there were the nightmares. She kept dreaming about the bloody daggers. She saw blood on her hands that wasn't there and couldn't wash it off. (You can't wash off something that is in your mind, can you? Try it sometime and see.)

She held up her hands and they were clean. The blood was all in her mind. I liked that bit. Nothing on the stage for me to mop up. But, as I said, the worst was still to come.

The audience in the White Swan yard had all had a lot to drink and wanted more. My jug was empty. I pushed back to the tap room and Master Foulbrew filled half of my jug with ale. Then he splashed in water from another barrel. 'You can't sell them water,' I argued.

'They've had so much to drink they'll never notice,' he snarled. 'They won't know.'

'I'll tell them,' I said.

His little red eyes went narrow. He started to unbuckle the belt around his huge gut.

I snatched up the jug of watery beer and ran. I filled jugs and gathered money till my apron was full of coins again.

I passed the door that led to a passage at the back of the stage and opened it. The boy who played Lady Macbeth had torn off his wig and wiping the sweat off his brow. He smiled when he saw me. 'Do you want some watery beer?' I asked.

He nodded. 'That's me finished now,' he said. 'Lady Macbeth goes off and falls off the castle walls to her death.'

'I know,' I said as I poured ale into a mug. 'I've watched it every evening this week. You're very good.' I felt myself blushing and felt foolish. He didn't seem to notice.

He shrugged. 'It's Master Shakespeare's words that are marvellous,' he said. He supped at the ale and wiped sweat off his brow. 'Wonderful. Thank you, Mary. I wish we could have a pot-girl with us every place we do our show. And expert stage-mopper,' he added with a grin.

'I wish I could come with you.'

He shook his head. 'I don't think we could afford you,' he sighed. But an idea was growing in my mind. I wasn't Macbeth – I couldn't kill to get my own way – but I could be bold and reckless as that player king.

'I'd better go. See you later,' I said.

The play

Outside of Macbeth's castle

The enemies of Macbeth are everywhere. His people in Scotland hate his harsh rule. Macduff wants to avenge the deaths of his family; Malcolm wants to avenge the death of his father, King Duncan. Their armies are gathered on the borders, ready to invade.

Macbeth believes he can't be beaten, the witches told him so. He tells his troops, 'We cannot lose till Birnam forest comes to Dunsinane.' He straps on his armour and prepares to meet the enemy attacks. They

cannot take the mighty castle. Macbeth's enemies will run out of food and starve before that happens.

But outside the castle Malcolm orders his men to each cut a branch from the trees in Birnam forest that they can hide behind as the creep up to the walls and climb them.

Then a servant brings terrible news – it strikes Macbeth's spirit like a broadsword to the heart. Lady Macbeth has fallen to her death as she walked in her sleep. Macbeth feels dead inside now Lady Macbeth is gone. Life is not worth living. **'Life is just a walking shadow,'** he sighs.

Then more news. A messenger enters and reports that he has seen an amazing sight – the woods of Dunsinane are moving toward the castle. Macbeth slaps the messenger, crying, **'You are a liar and slave!'**

But Macbeth knows the witches' tale is coming true. The end is close now. If he must die, he will die a brave soldier in battle: **'At least we'll die with harness on our back.'**

He won't hide in the shelter of his castle. He will go out and attack Malcom and Macduff.

The pot-girl's tale

This was the part of the play when everyone forgot to drink their ale. When I could stop and watch a fine battle on that little stage.

The actors worked so hard to make it look like a deadly fight – and still make sure they didn't hurt themselves.

They screamed their hate, swords slashed and shields crashed. Men whirled around with steel helmets, breast-plates, swords and daggers flashing in the light of the torches that lit the stage. Some clutched at pretend wounds and gave death gurgles as they staggered off.

The audience shouted – excited and waving their ale-pots till the thin beer splashed over the yard and over heads.

At last the stage is left to Macbeth and his greatest enemy, Macduff.

And I stood ready with my mop ...

The play

The battlefield

'Go Back, Macduff,' the beaten king cries. 'I have done you so much harm. I killed your wife and children. Do not make me kill you too.'

Macduff laughs wildly. 'Give up, you coward. We shall put you in a fairground show for freaks. We'll put a label round your neck that says, "Come and see the tyrant."'

Macduff charges at Macbeth and drives him back with fierce blows. Macbeth may be a mighty soldier but Macduff is driven on by rage and pain. Macbeth is forced to the ground and Macduff hacks the King's head off his shoulders.

The pot-girl's tale

That was the messiest part of the whole play. Master Shakespeare's stage manager had a model of the head of Macbeth – a painted ball stuffed with rags. The actor playing Macduff ran off stage after Macbeth. He picked up the dummy head, dipped it in the bucket of blood and carried it back onto the stage for the final scene.

Dripping.

The play

Macbeth's castle

Macduff finds Malcolm on the battlefield. Macbeth is dead and all his army have run away or given up the fight.

'Hail, King Malcolm,' Macduff cries. 'Because that's what you are now Macbeth is dead. Look, here I have his cursed head. Scotland is free.'

So Malcolm takes the crown and ends the reign of cruel Macbeth.

The pot-girl's tale

The audience cheered till the ground shook. The handsome young Henry who played Lady Macbeth stuck his wig back on his head to take his bow. The customers of the White Swan roared and even Master Foulbrew clapped his rough hands.

The torches were guttering out and the crowd started going home. The actors had large wicker baskets where they packed away their swords and armour, soldier boots and costumes.

I stepped onto the stage in the fading

light and mopped up the blood from Macbeth's head. It was the last show. They were driving off to Stratford in the morning, Henry said. The place where Master Shakespeare had been born. I'd miss them.

Master Fulbright stood and watched. 'There are pots to be washed before you crawl into your bed,' he shouted. My 'bed' was a scattering of straw in the loft of the inn, alive with rats and fleas. He went on, 'Then sweep up all the sawdust off the inn floor and clean the ashes from the fire.'

'It'll take me all night,' I wailed.

He shrugged. 'So? I pay you.'

'No you don't. You give me a filthy room and feed me with even filthier food. You are the meanest man in London and twice as cruel as King Macbeth. I wish it was your head on a pole.'

Silence. Only the crackle of dying

torches. A murmur of actors loading their wagon outside the door. Stillness. Then Master Foulbrew began to unbuckle his belt and march towards the stage, purple in the face. 'Come here, you ungrateful maggot, and I will whip you till the skin peels off your back.'

This time he meant it. I ran to the door at the back of the stage and pulled it open. I heard his heavy boots clatter over the stage towards me. Inside the door was my mop bucket. I meant to throw it under his feet to give me time to run. I swung it and let go. But ...

It wasn't my mop bucket. It was the bucket of pig's blood. It splashed under his boots. He stepped in the dark red slime and skidded. He waved his arms to try and balance himself but instead he shot forward and his head crashed into the doorpost.

He lay still. He was snorting softly. Not dead then.

But I'd be dead if I didn't get away. He groaned and started to awaken. I looked for somewhere to hide. There was one last costume basket waiting to be loaded onto the actors' wagon.

I lifted the lid and threw myself inside. Fur and silk soothed me while buttons scratched. I lay still.

'Last one,' I heard Henry say and felt the basket lifted into the air and carried out.

'Have you seen a girl?' I heard Foulbrew ask.

'What? The pretty pot-girl?' Henry replied.

'The weedy ratlet,' the inn-keeper croaked.

'She ran down towards the river, I think,' the actor said.

I heard Foulbrew's boots rattle on the cobbles as he ran, crying, 'She's got all my money. It's in her apron!'

And so it was.

The cart rocked and began the long

journey into the darkness. After a few moments the lid on my basket lifted. Henry looked in and smiled in the starlight. 'I said we needed a pot-girl to join us. Looks like we have one.'

'You said you couldn't afford one.'

'Maybe if she comes along with an apron full of money we can,' he laughed.

And that's how I came to join the players on their journeys to every corner of the country. And Henry? Ah, that's another story for another play. But the story of Henry and me didn't end in misery like Macbeth and his lady. Oh, no.

Some stories have happy endings.

Did you know?

Shakespeare's plays are so much fun to watch. People have laughed and cried, gasped and groaned at the plays for over 400 years. Why? Because Shakespeare knew what sort of stories people wanted to see. People still do.

Macbeth is ...

- A scary story. Macbeth kills the king to take his crown. Then he has to go on killing more and more people to hang on to the throne. He kills his best friend, Banquo, and even has the wife and little children of Macduff killed to teach his enemy a lesson. And at the end Macbeth's head (a dummy of course) is carried onto the stage. How scary is that?

• A thriller. After Macbeth kills the old king he and Lady Macbeth put the blame on the guards. Will they get away with murder? Yes, they will. But how long can Macbeth hide the truth? At last his enemies gather and attack. Who will win? We can't wait to find out.

• A comedy. Just when old King Duncan arrives at Macbeth's castle the doors are guarded by a gatekeeper. The man is drunk and rambles around the stage saying silly and rude things.

• A ghost story. Dead people rise up to appear on the stage. The most ghastly one is Banquo, whose ghost is covered in blood. But only Macbeth (and the people watching the play) see the horrible sight.

The other characters think Macbeth is going mad. Maybe he is.

• A magic story. The witches have magical powers. They can see Macbeth's future and tell him what is going to happen. But things don't work out the way Macbeth thinks they will. The witches say he will be king until Dunsinane Wood comes to his castle. Hah! That will never happen, he laughs. But it will, it does. How did the witches know? Wicked magic.

• A history story. 'Look at King Macbeth,' Shakespeare's is saying. 'This is what happens when a warrior becomes your king. He way be a great fighter but you don't want him on the throne. See what happened in real life?' (Sadly Shakespeare wasn't very good at history. The real King Macbeth of Scotland was not so evil as the one in the play ... and there were no witches or ghosts ... but they make a great story.)

What next?

Can you tell a scary story?

Shakespeare knew how to thrill us with a terrible tale. Maybe you could try it.

Work with a friend. See if you can each tell a story of ghosts, or witches, or magic, or a monstrous man. Can you make it so scary your friend's teeth rattle?

You don't have to write it all down.

Shakespeare's tales were for *telling* not for *writing*. But you could make some notes.

Terry Deary's top tip for story-making

Make sure you know the end of your story before you start. Sometimes I decide the last line of a story before I begin the first line. It helps stop me rambling.

Terry Deary's Shakespeare Tales

If you liked this book
why not look out for the rest of
Terry Deary's Shakespeare Tales?
Meet Shakespeare and his
theatre company!